HOOKED ON THE BOOK

Patrick's Adventures Through
The Books Of The Bible

PRESENTED TO

_____

By Liz and Jack Hagler

HOOKED ON THE BOOK permissions: HAGLER PUBLISHING, 22380 Berry Dr, Salinas, CA 93908
ISBN: 978-0-615-46549-4   HookedOnTheBook.com
Hooked On The Book: The Story of God's goodness in every book of the Bible.
Library of Congress Control Number : 2011936676
Publisher's Cataloging-in-Publication data is available.

ACKNOWLEDGMENTS
Special thanks to:
Tom, Carol, Barbara, the Bell's, Patty, and Cheryl for their insightful editing and support;
Bev, the Mejia's, and Diana, who have been cheerleaders and prayer partners;
The Mac Store guys, the computer graphics helpers;
Our parents who instilled in us the drive and discipline to stick with a project;
Our many other friends and family, you know who you are, who walked alongside us.

AND to our God who inspired men to write down His wonderful plan in THE BOOK.

Printed in CHINA
CPSIA Section 103(a) Compliant
www.beaconstar.com/consumer
ID: K0115482.
Tracking No.: L1312351-7951

First edition © 2011
10 9 8 7 6 5 4 3 2

For
Carrie,
Jenna,
and Nathan
We love you so much
we could *POP*!

CHAPTER 1

Whoever said that Saturdays are fun isn't named Patrick and doesn't live at 223 Eden Plains Road.

Saturdays are **B-O-R-I-N-G!**

So BORING, that one Saturday morning, I actually picked up a Bible!

5

GENESIS

Part 1

Pitch black **EVERYWHERE!**

"WHAT HAPPENED?" I cried!

"Moses is the name, and you've been hooked into Genesis, the first book of the Bible!"

"REALLY? IN THE BIBLE? I can't see a thing!"

"No problem, it will get light fast," said Moses. "This is the story of how the world began."

P.S. **Genesis** means "beginnings." Beginning of the world. Beginning of sin. Beginning of God's special nation.

IT MUST HAVE BEEN FANTASTIC WHEN YOU FLIPPED ON THE LIGHT, WHEN YOU STRETCHED THE HEAVENS WIDE, I WISH I'D SEEN THAT SIGHT!

WHEN YOU GAVE YOUR GENERAL'S ORDERS AND THE STARS MARCHED TO THEIR STANDS, WHEN THE SUN BLAZED BRIGHT ACROSS THE SKY JUST AT YOUR COMMANDS.

11

GENESIS

Part 3

Somehow I got zapped into another Genesis story. Not sure how, but it happened faster than I could blink.

"Think God was surprised by Adam and Eve's sin?" asked Moses. "NO! He has a BIG plan. Just wait! Right now check out their great-great-grandson, Abe! Soon his family is going to live in a beautiful land that God called the 'Promised Land.'"

HA HA

ANY STORY WITHOUT THAT SNAKE SOUNDS GREAT!

OLD ABE, YOU WERE A-LAUGHING WHEN GOD SAID YOU'D HAVE A SON. FOR YOUR WIFE WAS IN HER 90'S, NOT A GIRL OF 21. SURE, LONG AGO GOD SPOKE, "I'LL MAKE A NATION FROM YOUR CLAN!" BUT NOW, AT AGE 100, YOU'RE CHUCKLING AT GOD'S PLAN.

AREN'T MY SONS HANDSOME!

JACOB   REUBEN   SIMEON

Exodus

Part 1

"What happened to Genesis? Where's the Promised Land?" I wondered.

"Congratulations! You just book-hopped into Exodus," exclaimed Moses! "That Promised Land will come. Right now these great-great-grandkids of Isaac are slaves to the wicked Pharaoh in Egypt. God told me to speak to him!"

BY THE WAY, IF YOU WANT TO BOOGIE, THIS NEXT POEM MAKES A GREAT RAP!

GIVE IT UP PHARAOH!

A Pharaoh was like a king.

Moses wasn't concerned. He was busy carrying the Ten Commandments, rules God gave to His family.

WE HAVE FAMILY RULES, TOO - ON OUR REFRIGERATOR.

COUNT 'EM, 10!

GOD GAVE TO US A LOVE LETTER,
TEN RULES FOR ALL TO MIND.
HE COULD HAVE GIVEN FIFTY-FOUR,
OR PERHAPS A HUNDRED AND NINE.

BUT TEN IS JUST THE RIGHT AMOUNT,
THEY'RE HEAVY AS CAN BE.
IMAGINE CARRYING ONE HUNDRED RULES,
IT'D BE THE END OF ME!

EXODUS 20

TRANSLATION OF THE TEN COMMANDMENTS
1. Worship God only.
2. Don't worship things you make.
3. Honor God by word and deed.
4. Rest on God's day.
5. Honor your mom and dad.
6. Do not kill people.
7. Love your wife or husband.
8. Do not steal.
9. Do not lie.
10. Do not wish for other people's things.

"Speaking of rules," said Moses, "the guys in this book, called Priests, teach God's rules. Today they're getting anointed with oil. Watch it drip down their necks."

"GROSS!" I cried, "anointing looks gooey!"

23

CHAPTER 2
JOSHUA

"It's sad about Moses. I'll sure miss him," said a perky guy.

"Who are you?" I asked.

"I'm Joshua, the new leader God chose to conquer the Promised Land."

"Are you afraid?" I gulped.

"Nope, watch God smash the city of Jericho," he said.

OH!

24

JUDGES

"MORE CHAOS!" I cried. "I thought you already took the land?"

"We did. Then I died and the people forgot about God," said Joshua.

"NO WAY!" I replied.

"YES, WAY!" he continued. "God's enemies again took the land. New leaders, called Judges, helped folks get back to God. Some Judges were better than others."

All this fighting steamed up my glasses!

HI! I WAS A JUDGE THAT FOLLOWED GOD!

HI! I WAS A JUDGE THAT FOLLOWED GOD, TOO!

HI! I WAS A JUDGE THAT TRIED TO FOLLOW GOD BUT THEN MESSED UP!

TODAY YOU GET TO HEAR MY STORY. HERE'S THE PREVIEW!

DEBORAH   GIDEON   SAMSON

GOD TOLD ME NEVER TO CUT MY HAIR. IT GAVE ME SUPER STRENGTH. ONE DAY A BAD GIRLFRIEND DID JUST THAT.

WITHOUT MY SUPER STRENGTH, HER FRIENDS TOOK ME PRISONER. THEY CHAINED ME BETWEEN TWO PILLARS THAT HELD UP THEIR BUILDING.

GOD WASN'T HAPPY WITH THESE PEOPLE. I PRAYED TO DESTROY THEM.

CHECK OUT MY PRAYER ON THE NEXT PAGE...

GOOD THING I CAN STILL HEAR, BECAUSE I CAN'T SEE!

"Ready to hear about a female with fearless faith?" asked Joshua.

"A girl story, **UGH!**"
I decided to listen anyway.

NO BAD GUYS IN THIS BOOK? BUMMER!

The book of **Ruth** took place during the same time the Judges were leaders.

RUTH, RUTH,
FROM A FARAWAY LAND,
HAVE YOU LOST YOUR HUSBAND?
IS HE BURIED IN THE SAND?
WHY FOLLOW OLD NAOMI?
YOU WERE MARRIED TO HER SON.
BUT TO LEAVE BEHIND YOUR FAMILY,
IT MUST HAVE HURT A TON.

I'M GOING BACK TO MY HOME LAND.

WHERE YOU GO, I WILL GO!

I'M NAOMI'S RELATIVE NAMED BOAZ. YOU MAY PICK GRAIN FROM MY FIELD.

NICE!

RUTH PRAISED GOD AS SHE WORKED.

LATER ON...

WILL YOU MARRY ME?

YES, BOAZ. YES!

WHAT A FAITHFUL WIFE GOD GAVE ME!

RUTH, RUTH,
THE FAITHFUL ONE,
GOD BLESSED YOU GREATLY
WITH A HUSBAND AND A SON.
I WONDER IF IT'S POSSIBLE,
I WONDER CAN YOU SEE,
THAT THE GRANDFATHER OF KING DAVID
IS BOUNCING ON YOUR KNEE?

RUTH 4:13-22

Want to know who King David is?
He's just a book-hop away!

1 & 2 SAMUEL

"TA DA! INTRODUCING THE KINGS," proclaimed Joshua. "After the Judges, God's people wanted kings as their leaders. First there was King Saul, and then... drum roll please... KING DAVID!"

CAN YOU BELIEVE IT?
THAT'S A PICTURE OF ME,
SWINGING ALONE,
ON THIS BIG OLIVE TREE.

GOD SEEMS TO BE SEARCHING
FOR HEARTS LIKE MINE,
BUT HE SAYS RIGHT HERE
THEY'RE HARD TO FIND!

SURE, I POUNDED GOLIATH
WITH ONLY A PEBBLE,
AND JOTTED SOME PSALMS
IN THE CLEF CALLED TREBLE.

BUT 100% GOOD,
I JUST WAS NOT.
NO DAINTY DABBLER,
I SINNED A LOT!

I MURDERED A MAN
AND STOLE HIS WIFE.
BECAUSE OF MY SIN,
MY SON LOST HIS LIFE.

GOD CAN'T BE SEARCHING
FOR A PERFECT GUY.
IF HE WERE, HE'D SURELY
HAVE PASSED ME BY.

NOT POWER OR WEALTH,
WHAT CAN IT BE?
I'LL BET YOU KNOW.
WILL YOU TELL ME?

1 SAMUEL 16:7

1 & 2 KINGS

"King David's son, Solomon, was the next king," said Joshua. "He was miserable! Good and evil fought inside him."

"Who won?" I asked.

"Neither. It was a split decision!" Joshua chuckled.

SOLOMON EATS BREAKFAST WITH IDOLS

1&2 Chronicles

"In 1st and 2nd Chronicles, God's people were sad." said Joshua.

"WHY?" I questioned.

"Just like in Exodus, they were in slavery. God wanted to encourage them. He made it a game. Your job is to fill in the blanks."

CAN WE PLAY THE GAME, TOO?

WHAT COULD HAVE POSSESSED YOU TO THINK THAT I HAD LEFT YOU? IS THAT THE WAY I ACTED IN THE PAST?

WHEN _____ WAS A-STRESSIN', NO SOULMATE AS A BLESSIN'. I TOOK HIS BONE, AND WHITTLED OUT A WIFE!

Genesis
The beginning of the world.
The beginning of sin.
The beginning of God's special nation.

Exodus
The people are slaves in Egypt. Moses confronts Pharoah.
God's people leave Egypt and wander in the desert.
God gives the Ten Commandments.

Leviticus
God provides teachers to help them follow the Ten Commandments.

Numbers
More details on God's people still wandering in the desert. A new generation is born.

Deuteronomy
Moses says goodbye and reminds the people to love God as they go into their new land.

Joshua
God's people enter their Promised Land and start capturing the cities.

Judges
New leaders like Samson in the new land.

Ruth
One woman who trusts God. God blesses her.

1st and 2nd Samuel
God chooses imperfect kings like David to lead His people.

1st and 2nd Kings
David's son Solomon had a divided heart towards God.

1st and 2nd Chronicles
God's great review book.

I'VE GOT THE ANSWERS!

ADAM
ABRAHAM
RUTH

A NO SLEEP BLESSING!

WHEN _____ WAS A-STEWIN', NO SON TO HEAR BOO-HOOIN'. I BLESSED HIM WITH A BAWLING BABY BOY.

WHEN _____ WAS A-PRAYIN', WITH NAOMI I'M A STAYIN'. I GAVE HER BOTH A HUSBAND AND A SON.

FOLKS, WHAT'S WITH THIS THINKING? CHARGE AHEAD AND STOP YOUR SHRINKING. I'M JUST AS GREAT AT HELPING YOU TODAY.

IF YOU'LL REMEMBER ALL THAT'S PAST, AND MY DEEDS THAT ALWAYS LAST, THOSE GLOOMY THOUGHTS WILL POP AND BLOW AWAY.

THERE ONCE WAS A PRIEST
WHO CRIED AND CRIED,
THEN YANKED OUT A CLUMP OF HIS HAIR.
HE PULLED OUT A WAD
OF HIS LITTLE BROWN BEARD
AND THREW UP BOTH ARMS IN DESPAIR.

THIS PRIEST WAS A WRECK
AS HE WATCHED GOD'S FOLKS SIN.
HE CRIED OUT TO GOD ALL THAT EVE,
"FORGIVE US, OH LORD,
I'M ASHAMED AND EMBARRASSED,
I'M SURE THAT YOU MUST BE QUITE PEEVED."

BUT HIS STORY TAKES A TWIST,
I'M THRILLED TO REPORT,
THE FOLKS OVERHEAR AND REPENT.
THAT'S VERY GOOD NEWS
FOR ONE LITTLE PRIEST,
FOR HE'S **ME** AND MY ENERGY'S SPENT.

EZRA 9 & 10

WE WORSHIP YOU,
OH, STATUE!

When someone repents, they tell God they are sorry. Then they do the right thing!

37

NEHEMIAH

"LOOK OUT!" King David yelled as a foot whizzed by my chin.

"Wow, that was close," I exclaimed.

"After Ezra the Priest came Nehemiah the cheerleader," said King David. "He encouraged God's people to rebuild the wall around their city. Their enemies had destroyed it."

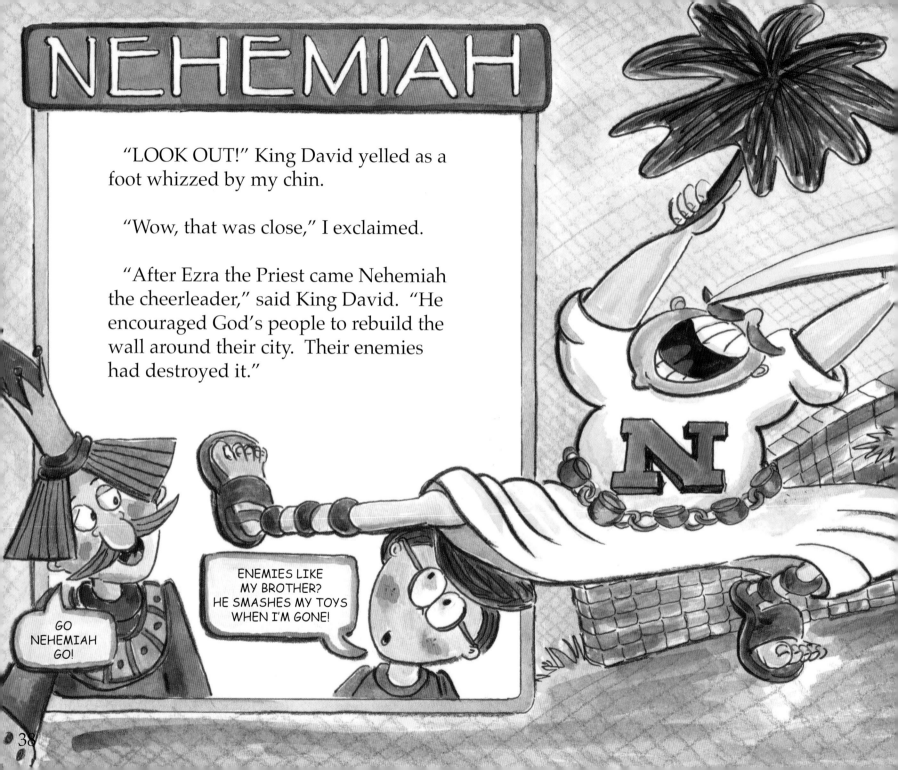

"You'll like this story," King David said. "It takes place back when God's people were slaves in the foreign land. An evil man tricked the king of this land. He said God's people threatened his kingdom. 'WIPE THEM OUT!' declared the king. He didn't know his wife Queen Esther was one of God's people.

Watch what happened!"

God's people are also called Jews!

HI, I'M THE QUEEN
NAMED ESTHER,
AND FINALLY I KNOW WHY!
GOD CROWNED ME, MRS. QUEEN
SO NOT ONE JEW WOULD DIE.

MY HUSBAND, MR. KING,
WAS TRICKED THE OTHER DAY
TO SIGN A PROCLAMATION:
WITH JEWS, BE DONE AWAY!

THIS MORNING,
COUSIN MORDECAI SAID,
"ESTHER, TELL THE KING,
HE'S MARRIED TO A JEW.
YOU WEAR HIS WEDDING RING!"

THEN I PUT MY HAIR IN BRAIDS
WITH BEADS AND BOWS PURE GOLD,
DRAPED MY ARM WITH SILKS
AND PERFUMES RARE AND BOLD.

JUST SIGN IT!

ALL JEWS, DO NOW AWAY!

THIS IS WHY GOD MADE YOU QUEEN. FOR THIS EXACT MOMENT!

I LIKE THIS PERFUME!

"Recognize that guy?" asked King David.

"He does look familiar," I said.

"His name starts with a D," grinned D-A-V-I-D. "My friends and I wrote 150 songs to God in this book. Just can't get enough of singing His praises!"

I'd never thought of praising God like this. It looked like fun!

I'M STROKING A HARP
THAT'S RIGGED TO A CHAIR
THAT'S BANGING A DRUM
THAT'S SHAPED LIKE A PEAR.

I KNOW THAT SOMETIMES
I'M A LITTLE OFF KEY
FROM STRUMMING A LYRE
WITH THE BONE OF MY KNEE.

BUT GOD, I CAN'T HELP IT!
I MUST PRAISE EVERYDAY.
I'LL BE SINGIN' AND DANCIN'
'TILL THEY HAUL ME AWAY!

PSALMS 150

I LOOK TO YOU GOD! PSALM 123:1

GOD LIVES! I PRAISE YOU, FOR YOU NEVER CHANGE! PSALM 18:46

"HUNGRY?" King David asked when we came to the book called Proverbs. "Just in time for a fresh batch of wisdom nuggets, right out of the oven. My son Solomon is quite the chef. These nuggets are his specialty!"

"Yumm!" I gobbled down three or four of them. They tasted amazing. David said they were even good for me.

WISDOM AND KNOWLEDGE FOR TODAY!

FOR THOSE WHO STAND THERE ASKING,
WHAT DO I DO TO BE WISE?
I SAY, MUNCH ON A PROVERB,
THAT'S WHAT I'D ADVISE!

THEY'RE A BIT LIKE HEALTHY VITAMINS,
DEHYDRATED BITS OF TRUTH,
PACKED FULL OF ACTIVE NUTRIENTS
TO TINGLE EVERY TOOTH.

THERE'S WISDOM AND LOTS OF KNOWLEDGE
IN VITAMINS W AND K,
BUILDING UP YOUR BRAIN CELLS
TO GUIDE YOU THROUGH YOUR DAY.

SO, THOSE WHO YEARN FOR WISDOM,
TAKE A PROVERB, YOU'LL FEEL TIP-TOP.
AND ONCE YOU TASTE THESE NUGGETS,
YOU'LL NEVER WANT TO STOP!

PROVERBS 1: 5-7

MONDAY'S HOUSE IS FULL OF FEMALES! **BORING!**

BLUE SMOKE **SO** WHAT!!

SAME OLD, SAME OLD.

CONSIDER ME, SOLOMON,
I'M SWIMMING IN GOLD.
BEING RICH ISN'T EASY,
IT LEAVES MY HEART COLD.

I'VE BUILT HANDSOME HOUSES
FOR EACH DAY OF THE WEEK.
MY CHARIOTS CHARGE FAST,
THEY CARVE OUT A BLUE STREAK.

I'VE THROWN BIRTHDAY PARTIES
WITH TEN BRANDS OF PUNCH.
WE ATE GOOEY DESSERTS
AND SKIPPED OUT ON LUNCH.

BUT WHEN ALL WAS OVER,
WHEN ALL WAS THROUGH,
ALL I HAD DONE
WASN'T ANYTHING NEW.

THERE'S A SECRET I'VE LEARNED,
AND I'M TELLING YOU TRUE,
HAPPINESS ISN'T FOUND
IN WHAT MONEY BUYS YOU.

IT'S WHEN WE SERVE GOD
AND LET HIM LEAD OUR LIVES,
THAT OUR SOULS LEAP FOR JOY
AND START SLAPPING HIGH FIVES.

I'M YOURS GOD! ONLY YOU CAN MAKE ME TRULY HAPPY!

ECCLESIASTES 2:24; 12:13

I MADE PARKS AND FILLED THEM WITH ALL KINDS OF FRUIT TREES.

I'M SO SICK OF DATES!

I OWNED GREAT HERDS AND FLOCKS!

I HIRED WONDERFUL SINGERS

I NEED SOME QUIET!

49

Song of Solomon

"They're kissing, how DISGUSTING!" I grumbled.

King David chuckled, "Solomon and his beautiful bride are so in love they can't help it."

"YUCK! Please don't tell my friends that I visited this book," I pleaded.

King David assured me he'd keep quiet. "But someday," he smiled, "you might like this book!"

I DOUBT IT!

CHAPTER 4

"What happened to the new book and the new guide?" I said to a big wooden sign. "Maybe you're my next clue."

I decided to check it out.

What Do Prophets Do?
1. Tell people what God says.

2. Tell people their future blessings if they obey God.

3. Tell people their future doom if they disobey God.

WELCOME TO THE PROPHETS!

RUNNING AN ERRAND

BACK SOON!

- Daniel -

ADVENTURE INSTRUCTIONS

THE VIS...
THE WEEPI...
UNPOP...
PRO...
ERR...
LOVE...
WIN...

① MEET EACH PROPHET!

② MATCH EACH PROPHET'S NICKNAME TO HIS BOOK!

SEE YOU AT THE END!

SCARY... I'M ON MY OWN. BUT I CAN DO THIS!

CHAPTER 5

KERPLUNK! I landed in the New Testament, dizzy. After all, I had just spun through 400 years of history in 4 seconds.

"Hi, I'm Matthew. Welcome to my book. This is the story of baby Jesus, God's Son, a new kind of king."

"How did you like the story of this king born in a cave?" asked Matthew.

"Jesus a king? Don't kings have fancy clothes and golden crowns?" I questioned.

"Not Jesus! He's a heavenly king. He came to serve rather than be served," continued Matthew.

MARK

I'M MARK WITH GOD'S SERVANT STORY.

JESUS WAS SPEAKING
ON A SANDY SHORE
TO 5,000 FOLKS,
MAYBE A TAD-BIT MORE.

THEY STOOD ALL DAY,
WISHING HE'D NEVER BE DONE.
THEIR STOMACHS WERE GROWLING,
ONE BY ONE.

" I HEAR," SPOKE JESUS.
"IT'S TIME TO MUNCH!"
HE TURNED TO A BOY,
"WILL YOU LOAN ME YOUR LUNCH?"

HE BROKE THE BOY'S BREAD
AND BLESSED HIS FISH,
FEEDING THAT CROWD,
FROM ONE LITTLE DISH!

MARK 6:30-44

63

"Time to hear about Jesus' human side from Luke the doctor," Matthew said. "How he died just like all men!"

"That makes me sad," I said.

"It made me sad, too," replied Matthew. "In fact all his friends were sad until we found out why he had to die."

JESUS HAD A LITTLE PARTY,
INVITED JUST TWELVE GUESTS.
HE SERVED THEM IN THE UPPER ROOM,
A PLACE THAT GOD HAD BLESSED!

HE FED THEM ALL SOME BREAD AND WINE,
AND TOLD A STORY OR TWO.
HE SAID THAT HE WAS GOING AWAY.
THEY ALL CRIED, "**BOO, HOO, HOO**!"

LUKE 22: 7-20

WHY JESUS HAD TO DIE!

ADAM AND EVE BROUGHT SIN INTO THE WORLD. (SEE GENESIS)

SO EVERYONE SINNED.

GOD WAS SAD ABOUT PEOPLE'S SIN.

GOD SENT JESUS TO DIE TO RECEIVE THE PUNISHMENT FOR EVERYONE'S SIN.

NOW GOD IS HAPPY THAT EVERYONE CAN BE FORGIVEN.

PEOPLE CAN BE HAPPY, TOO WHEN THEY BELIEVE JESUS DIED FOR THEIR SIN AND THEY ARE FORGIVEN.

P.S. REMEMBER, A SIN IS ANYTHING WE DO OR DON'T DO THAT DISPLEASES GOD.

JOHN

"I GET IT! Jesus the King died for MY sin...**AWESOME!**" I said.

"What's more, Jesus even came back to life," Matthew exclaimed!

JOHN

COOL!

DOUBLE-DOUBTING THOMAS WAS STUBBORN, THERE'S NO DOUBT. SUCKING ON HIS PINKIE, HE SHOOK HIS HEAD ABOUT.

HE SCOFFED, "I CAN'T BELIEVE CHRIST ROSE UP FROM THE DEAD. NOT UNLESS MY FINGERS TOUCH HIS BLOOD THAT'S RED."

THOMAS, I SAW JESUS TODAY!

GIVE ME A BREAK!

66

SWOOOSH!

"What's that?" I asked.

"It's the Holy Spirit here to give us power," said Matthew. "After Jesus left for heaven, he sent the Holy Spirit to help us. Dr. Luke tells this story."

Good thing there's a doctor close by. The Holy Spirit's flame of fire nearly burned one guy's head.

68

CHAPTER 6

Paul arrived jumping up and down with excitement.

"New Christians need guidance," he said. "These books will help them solve their problems. Can you count them? I always forget how many there are."

SURE I CAN EVEN NUMBER THEM!

P.S. Each book gets its name from the city or person I was writing to.

TO THE CHURCH THAT PAUL HELP BUILD

ROMANS

I'M SENDING YOU A BLUEPRINT MARKED "FIRST CLASS EXPRESS," TO HELP YOU BUILD YOUR CHURCH TO MAKE IT A SUCCESS!
ROMANS 1:8-17

GREAT PLAN PAUL!

1. CHRIST DIED FOR YOU. YOU'RE NOW FORGIVEN,

GOD'S PLAN ROMANS 6:23

4. FAITH IN GOD IS KEY!

3. YOU'RE MEMBERS OF GOD'S FAMILY,

2. HIS SPIRIT SETS YOU FREE.

I

Galatians

FOUR

RULE #51
#202
RULE #24
#59
RULE #34
2
#6

YOU ARE SAVED FROM YOUR SINS BY KEEPING THESE RULES.

THESE RULES ARE TOO HEAVY!

THANKS, PAUL! WE'RE OUT OF HERE! JESUS DIED FOR OUR SINS!

I HEAR YOU'RE LETTING HEAVY RULES BE LOADED ON YOUR BACK. THEY WEIGH A TON AND SHIFT YOUR SPINE AND MAKE YOUR TAILBONE CRACK.

I HEAR SOME MEN HAVE TWEAKED YOUR BRAINS. THEY SAY CHRIST'S GIFTS AREN'T FREE. UNLESS YOU'RE INTO MASSIVE GUILT, I'D DROP THOSE WEIGHTS AND FLEE.

GALATIANS 3:1-5

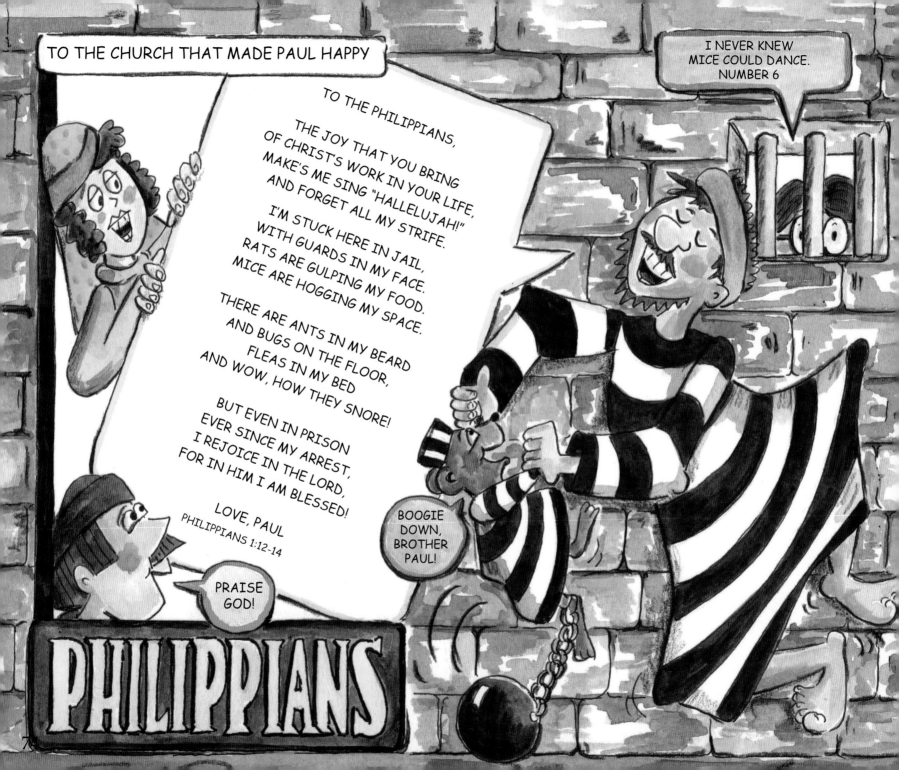

"How many books so far?" asked Paul.

"I only have one thumb left. So, I guess that makes nine," I replied.

"Start using your toes," he continued. "Here are a few more books I wrote to friends."

10 AND 11

1&2 TIMOTHY

TO PAUL'S YOUNG FRIEND

HE'S SO YOUNG!

IT'S AWFUL HARD
FOR ME TO IMAGINE,
HOW LIFE MUST BE FOR YOU.
A TIMID, FRECKLED,
YOUTHFUL GUY
WITH A GIANT JOB TO DO.

YOU'RE OVERWHELMED,
YOUR BRAIN'S A BLUR
WITH THE DETAILS OF YOUR TASK.
JUST HOW'S ONE KID
TO LEAD A CHURCH,
AND DO ALL THAT GOD WOULD ASK?

HERE'S SOME NOTES
I'VE JOTTED DOWN,
FOR READING AT BEDTIME.
SOME THOUGHTS FOR YOU,
TO GET YOU THROUGH,
UNTIL YOU HIT YOUR PRIME.

THANKS, PAUL! I NEEDED SOME HELP!

1 TIMOTHY 4:12-16

77

"That was a rough landing!" I cried. "I'm not sure how many more like that I can take."

My new guide, John, encouraged me. "Keep the faith, only a few more books left. These books are all about faith. Hebrews is where the great faith guys hang out!"

THAT LANDING WAS WORSE THAN THE ONE IN MATTHEW.

HEBREWS

LET ME TELL YOU THE STORY OF GOD'S GREAT FAITH FOLK. WHEN GOD SAID, "OBEY," THEY DID WHAT HE SPOKE.

FIRST NOD AT NOAH WHOSE FAITH BUILT AN ARK. THEN ADMIRE ABRAHAM, THE FIRST PATRIARCH.

NOW MUSE OVER MOSES, WHO BY FAITH SPLIT THE SEA. AND DELIGHT IN KING DAVID, WHO WROTE HISTORY.

GREAT WALL OF FAITH

83

"Those guys were tough!" I cried.

"PRAISE GOD FOR THEIR FAITH," John declared. "Peter wrote this book to cheer them on."

LOOKS PAINFUL!

THOUGH A ROCK HITS YOUR SOCK
AND SEVERS A NERVE,
THOUGH YOU'RE JABBED OR STABBED
BY THOSE WHOM YOU SERVE,

THOUGH THEY BREAK BOTH YOUR ARMS
AND TWIST UP YOUR LEGS,
THOUGH THEY TIE-DYE YOUR HAIR
WITH SOME ROTTEN, RAW EGGS,

AS YOU BANDAGE EACH OTHER
FROM HEAD DOWN TO TOE,
SING YOUR PRAISES TO JESUS,
"LA, LA, LA," DOSEY DOE.

MAKE MUSIC TO HEAVEN.
THANK GOD FOR YOUR PAIN.
YOU'RE LOOKIN' LIKE JESUS,
NO NEED TO COMPLAIN.

1 PETER 4:12,13

85

"Time for *my* faith books," announced John. "Tricky teachers wanted to steal people's faith in Jesus. God's folks need to **BEWARE!**"

This did look tricky.

HOW CAN YOU TELL
A TRICKY TEACHER
WHEN ONE'S KNOCKING AT YOUR DOOR?
DO THEY HOLD A CUP
WITH HANDS OUTSTRETCHED,
BEGGING LIKE THEY'RE POOR?

DO THEY WEAR BOW TIES,
CRISP WHITE SHIRTS,
AND CARRY BIG BLACK BOOKS,
OR HAVE A MASK
AND FLOWING CAPE,
AND GIVE OFF SCARY LOOKS?
NO!
WHEN LOOKING OUT YOUR PEEP HOLE,
YOU CAN'T TELL WHOSE TEACHING'S TRUE.
JUST ASK A SIMPLE QUESTION:
"WHO IS JESUS CHRIST TO YOU?"

1 JOHN 2:22-23 AND 2 JOHN 1:7-11

REVELATION

"THE LAST BOOK! BOO HOO," I cried.

John spoke up, "I think God saved the best part for last. This book is a vision He gave me of Jesus coming back to earth to conquer all evil."

"Really? All evil?" I exclaimed. "I like that ending!"

PRETTY EXCITING HUH!

IT'S STILL AMAZING
WHEN I THINK OF IT,
THE VISION I SAW THAT DAY,
CHRIST BURSTING THROUGH
THE PUFFY CLOUDS,
IT TOOK MY BREATH AWAY!

HE SAT ASTRIDE
A SNOW-WHITE HORSE,
GRAND ARMIES CHARGED BEHIND,
PASSIONATELY PRANCING
AND LOUDLY SNORTING,
A SIGHT TO BLOW MY MIND!

REVELATION 19:11-16

Revelation
The revelation of Jesus Christ, which God sent to reveal what will happen in the future. He sent an angel John so

Unfortunately, there was no time to stare. *For in an instant...*

93

QUESTIONS FOR GOD

For a free video curriculum and to order additional copies, check out

www.HookedOnTheBook.com

Liz Hagler is the illustrator of
The Bible Animal Storybook. Author Mack Thomas, Sisters, Oregon: Questar Publishing 1990,
and *The Early Reader's Bible.* Author V. Gilbert Beers, Sisters, Oregon: Questar Publishing 1991.
She has a BA in Art and English from the University of California at Davis and
studied graphic design at California College of Arts and Crafts.
She has also taught Sunday School for many years and home schooled her three children.

Jack Hagler is a pastor, teacher, executive coach, senior project manager,
homeschool principal and co-founder of Hagler Publishing.
Jack received his BS degree from the University of California at Berkeley
and his MDiv from Western Seminary.

Jack and Liz make their home in Salinas, California.
It is their great passion that kids of all ages get hooked on THE BOOK!